DON'T
WAIT UP

Reg Smythe

ℛℛ
RAVETTE BOOKS

This edition first published by Ravette Books Limited 1992.

Printed and bound
for Ravette Books Limited
3 Glenside Estate, Star Road, Partridge Green,
Horsham, West Sussex RH13 8RA
An Egmont Company
by Stige Arti Grafiche, Italy

ISBN: 1 85304 398 2

CUTTING OUT THE HAIRDO AND BINGO WOULD BE A START—

Smythe

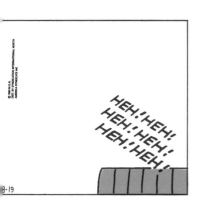

YOU'RE ALWAYS PICKING ON *ME*. JUST FOR A CHANGE, HOW ABOUT SAVING SOMEBODY ELSE FROM SIN?

YOU'LL NOTICE THAT I NEVER HAVE OCCASION TO HAVE A GO AT PERCY ABOUT IT—

THAT'S OKAY, FLO – I WASN'T ANNOYED, JUST INTRIGUED –

12-16

WHEN HE STOOD UP AND CLAPPED – WAS IT MY CLEVER SERMON OR JUST THE FACT THAT IT WAS OVER?

THAT'S A QUESTION HE OFTEN ASKS, AND NEVER STAYS FOR AN ANSWER

RIGHT, LET'S HEAR IT~!

WELL, IT WAS LIKE THIS, RUBY —

FORGET IT! IF YOU CAN'T GET MY NAME RIGHT THE REST OF YOUR TALE ISN'T GOING TO BE MUCH GOOD, EITHER!

© 1991 M.G.N.
DIST. BY SYNDICATION INTERNATIONAL NORTH AMERICA SYNDICATE INC.

SEE THAT?
NOT
A WORD

5-12

THE THINGS THAT THIS LAD PRAYS FOR I GENERALLY HAVE TO *PAY* FOR

9-4

I TRUST YOU'RE NOT PUTTING THE LASS OFF ME —

JUST THE REVERSE

ANOTHER THING IN HIS FAVOUR IS THAT YOU WON'T MIND DITCHING HIM IF SOMEONE ELSE COMES ALONG